MUSIC AND LYRICS BY

IRVING BERLIN

SELECTIONS FROM

THE MUSICAL

BASED ON
RKO's
MOTION PICTURE

PHOTOGRAPHS OF THE ORIGINAL PRODUCTION BY ALASTAIR MUIR

KENNETH H WAX
STEWART F LANE / BONNIE COMLEY, TED HARTLEY,
FLORA SUK-HWA YOON & LEE MENZIES

PRESENT
THE WORLD PREMIERE OF

TOP HAT

MUSIC AND LYRICS BY
IRVING BERLIN

BASED ON
RKO'S MOTION PICTURE

ADAPTED FOR THE STAGE BY
MATTHEW WHITE AND HOWARD JACQUES

ADVERTISING, MARKETING AND GRAPHICS – DEWYNTERS
NATIONAL PRESS – PREMIER PR
MARKETING CONSULTANT – HELEN SNELL
CASTING – JAMES HOPSON FOR PIPPA AILION
GENERAL MANAGEMENT – KENNY WAX LTD
PRODUCTION MANAGER – PATRICK MOLONY
ORCHESTRATIONS & ARRANGEMENTS – CHRIS WALKER
MUSICAL SUPERVISOR – RICHARD BALCOMBE
MUSICAL DIRECTOR – DAN JACKSON
LIGHTING DESIGNER – PETER MUMFORD
SOUND DESIGNER – GARETH OWEN
HAIR & WIGS – CAMPBELL YOUNG
SET DESIGNER – HILDEGARD BECHTLER
COSTUME DESIGNER – JON MORRELL
CHOREOGRAPHER – BILL DREAMER
DIRECTOR – MATTHEW WHITE

BASED ON THE SCREENPLAY BY DWIGHT TAYLOR & ALLAN SCOTT

PRESENTED IN ARRANGEMENT WITH RKO PICTURES LLC,
WARNER BROS. THEATRE VENTURES INC. AND THE IRVING BERLIN MUSIC COMPANY

WWW.TOPHATONSTAGE.COM

FIRST PERFORMED AT MILTON KEYNES THEATRE, UK ON 16TH AUGUST 2011
OPENED IN THE WEST END AT THE ALDWYCH THEATRE, LONDON UK ON 9TH MAY 2012

MUSIC AND LYRICS BY

IRVING BERLIN

THE MUSICAL

BASED ON
RKO's
MOTION PICTURE

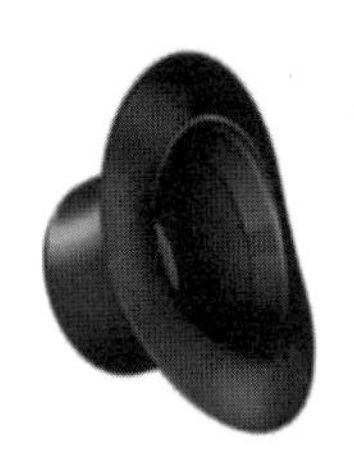

WISE PUBLICATIONS
PART OF THE MUSIC SALES GROUP
LONDON / NEW YORK / PARIS / SYDNEY / COPENHAGEN / BERLIN / MADRID / HONG KONG / TOKYO

PUBLISHED BY
WISE PUBLICATIONS
14-15 BERNERS STREET, LONDON W1T 3LJ, UK.

EXCLUSIVE DISTRIBUTORS:
MUSIC SALES LIMITED
DISTRIBUTION CENTRE, NEWMARKET ROAD,
BURY ST EDMUNDS, SUFFOLK IP33 3YB, UK.

MUSIC SALES PTY LIMITED
20 RESOLUTION DRIVE, CARINGBAH,
NSW 2229, AUSTRALIA.

ORDER NO. AM1004927
ISBN: 978-1-78038-630-0

PROJECT MANAGER: TOM FARNCOMBE.
MUSIC PROCESSED BY PAUL EWERS MUSIC DESIGN.
EDITED BY RUTH POWER.
DESIGN BY DEWYNTERS.
ARTWORK COURTESY OF KENNY WAX LTD.
PRINTED IN THE EU.

LIKE IRVING BERLIN ON FACEBOOK AT
WWW.FACEBOOK.COM/IRVINGBERLIN

LEARN MORE ABOUT IRVING BERLIN AT
WWW.IRVINGBERLIN.COM AND WWW.RNH.COM

FOLLOW RODGERS & HAMMERSTEIN ON
TWITTER @RNH_ORG FOR UPDATES
ON IRVING BERLIN'S SHOWS AND MUSIC.

WWW.TOPHATONSTAGE.COM

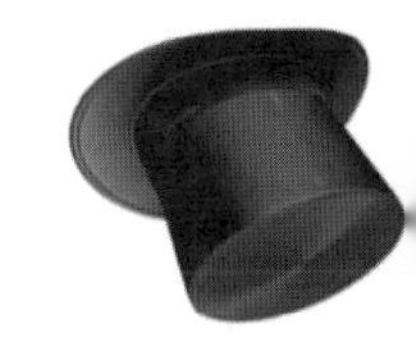

BETTER LUCK NEXT TIME

WORDS & MUSIC BY IRVING BERLIN

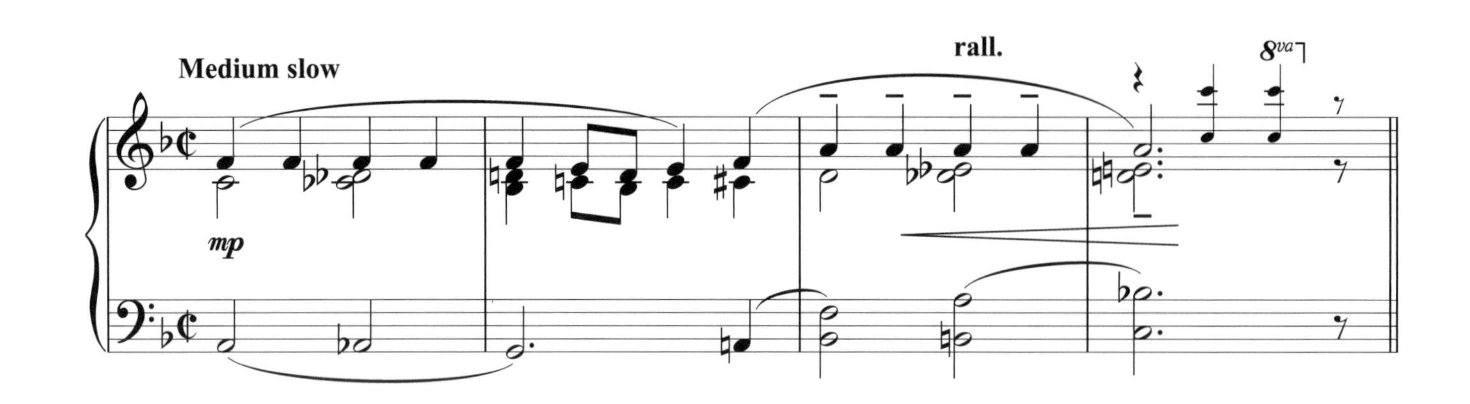

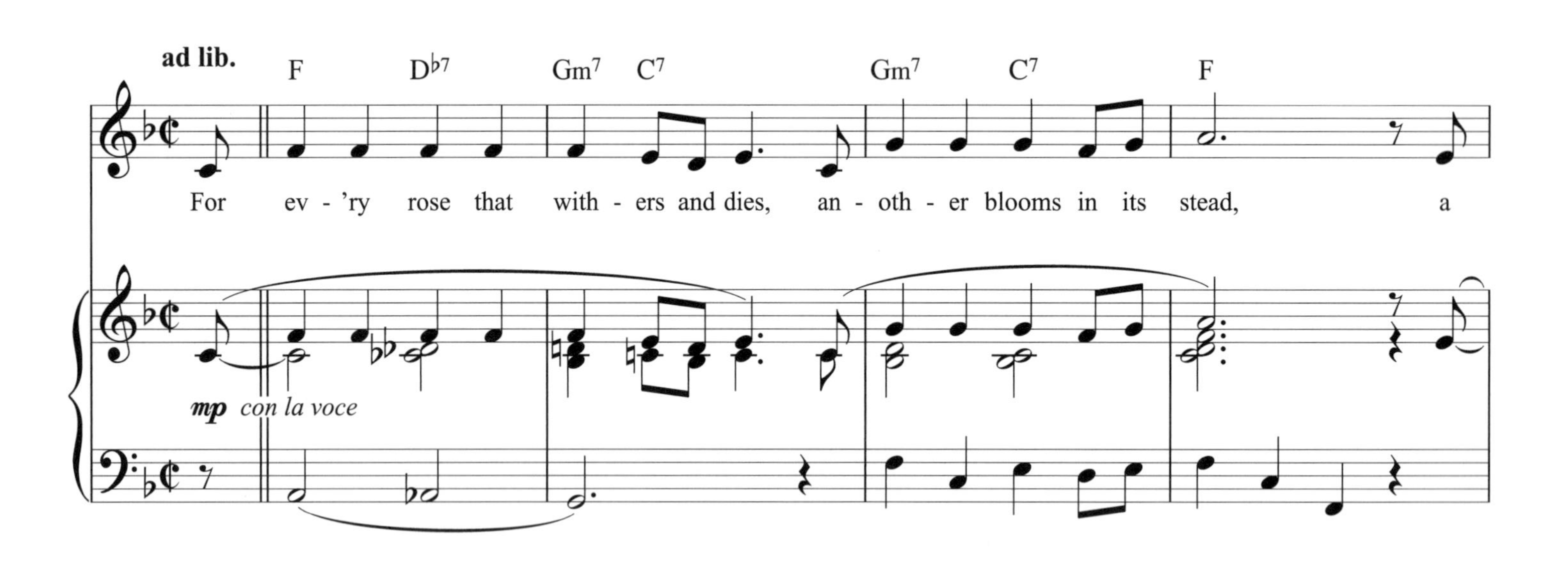

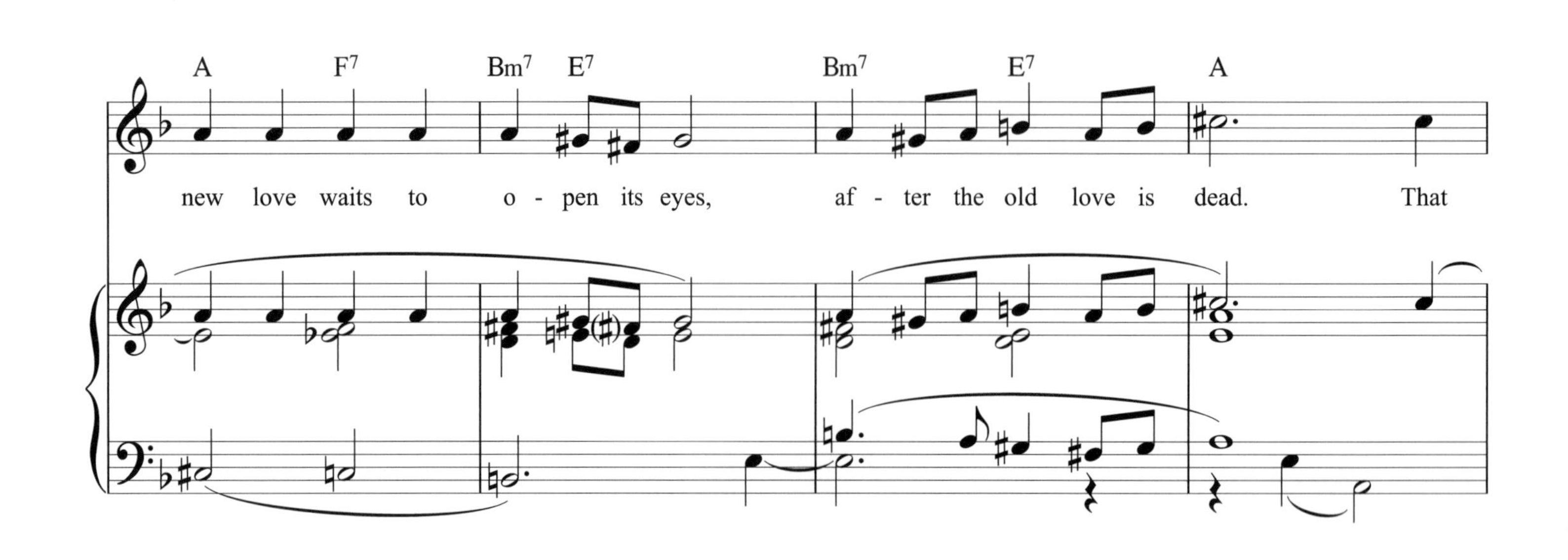

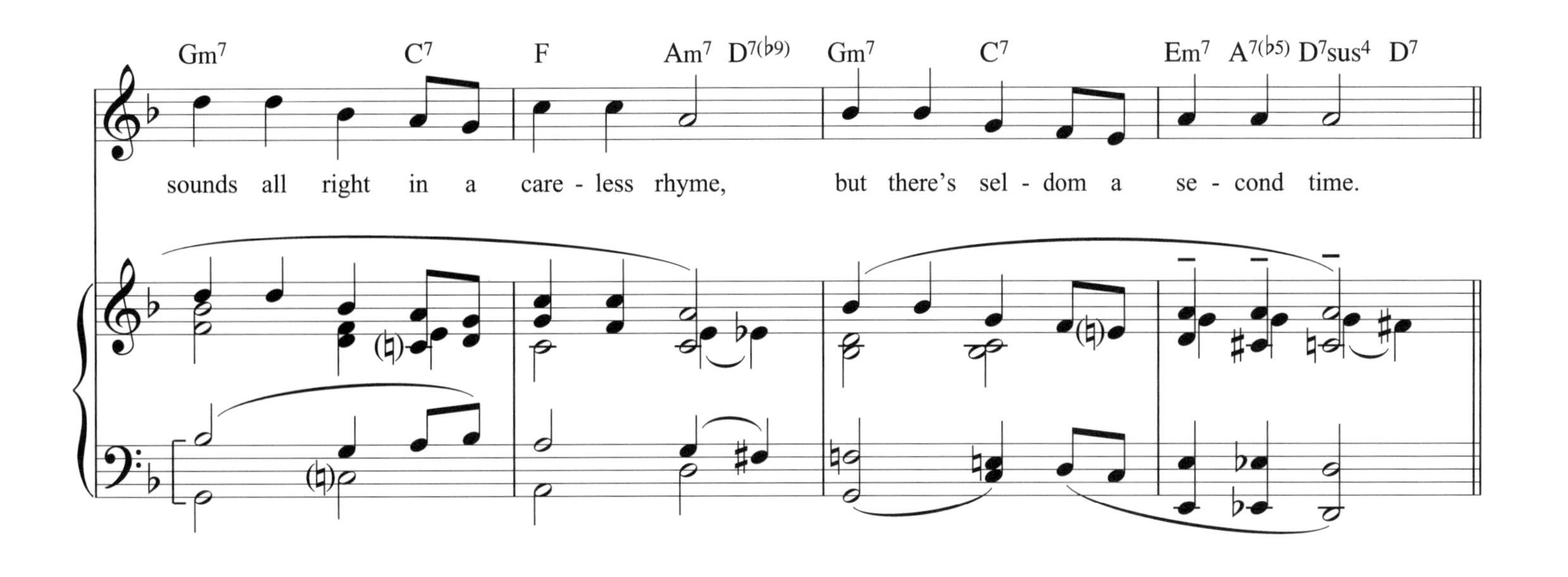
Gm7 C7 F Am7 D7(♭9) Gm7 C7 Em7 A7(♭5) D7sus4 D7
sounds all right in a care - less rhyme, but there's sel - dom a se - cond time.

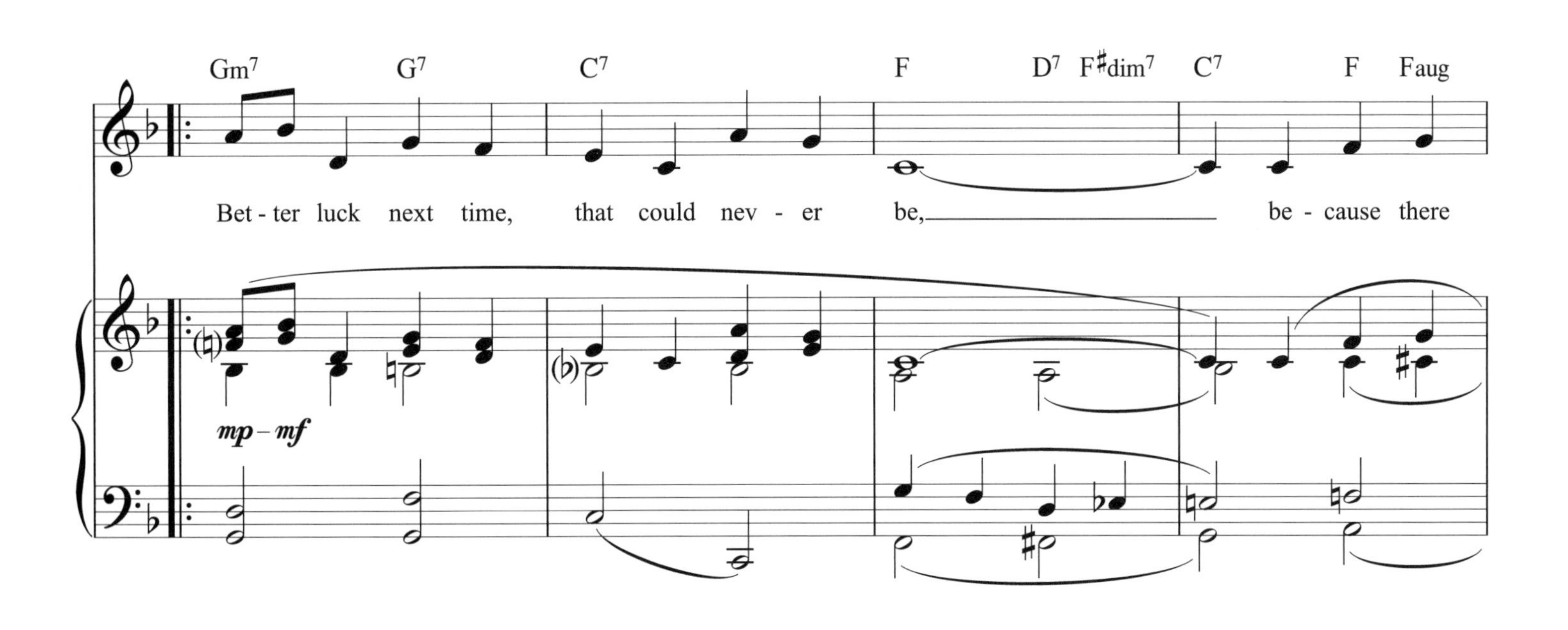
Gm7 G7 C7 F D7 F♯dim7 C7 F Faug
Bet - ter luck next time, that could nev - er be, be - cause there
mp - mf

B♭ G7 Bdim7 C7 C7(♭9) F Dm7 Gm7 C7aug(♭9)
won't ev - er be a next time for me, not for me.

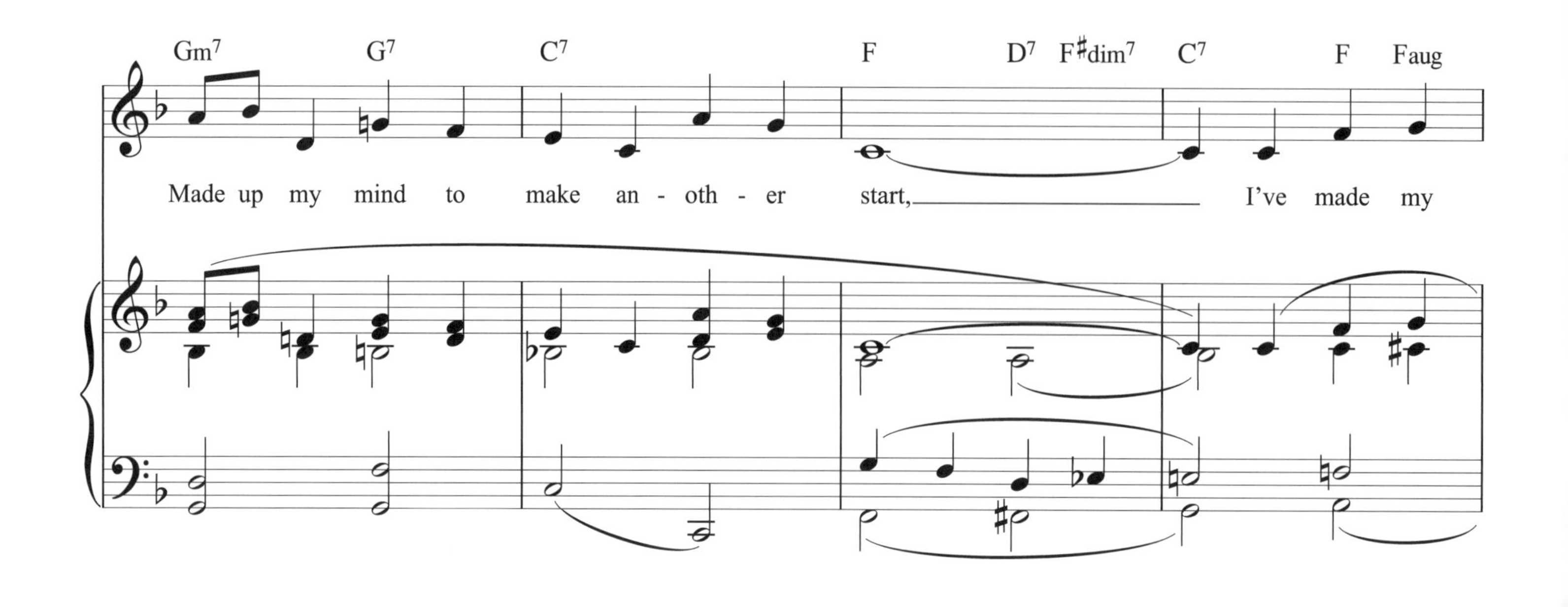
Gm7 G7 C7 F D7 F♯dim7 C7 F Faug
Made up my mind to make an - oth - er start, I've made my

B♭ G7 Bdim7 C7 C7(♭9) F Gm7 C7(♭9) F Dm7 F♯m
mind up but I can't make up my heart. I'd like a

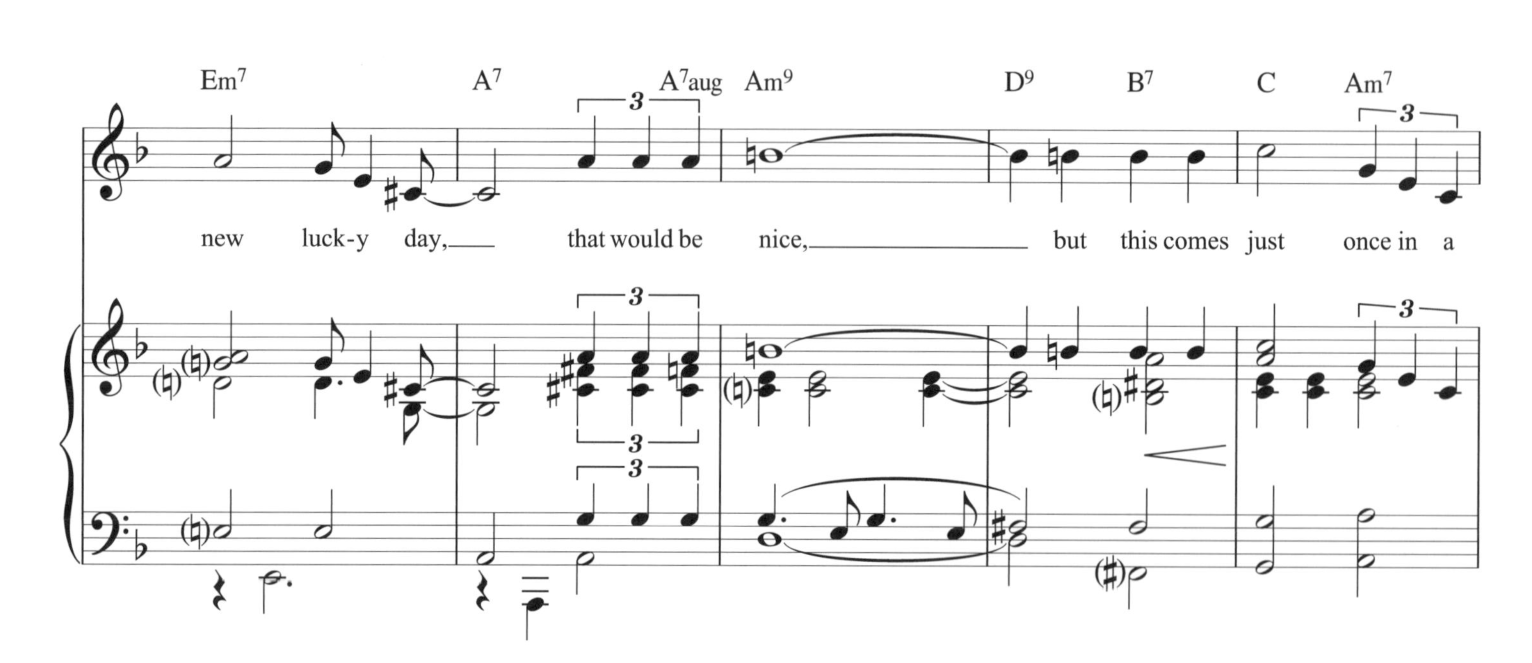
Em7 A7 A7aug Am9 D9 B7 C Am7
new luck-y day, that would be nice, but this comes just once in a
3
3
3
3
3

Dm7 G7 C7 Gm7 C7 Gm7 C9 C7aug(♭9) Gm7 G7 C7 B♭m C7(♭9)
life - time, not twice. So don't say "bet - ter luck next time" that could nev - er

Am7 D7 D7aug(♭9) F♯dim7 Gm7 B♭m F C9
be, be - cause there won't ev - er be a next time for

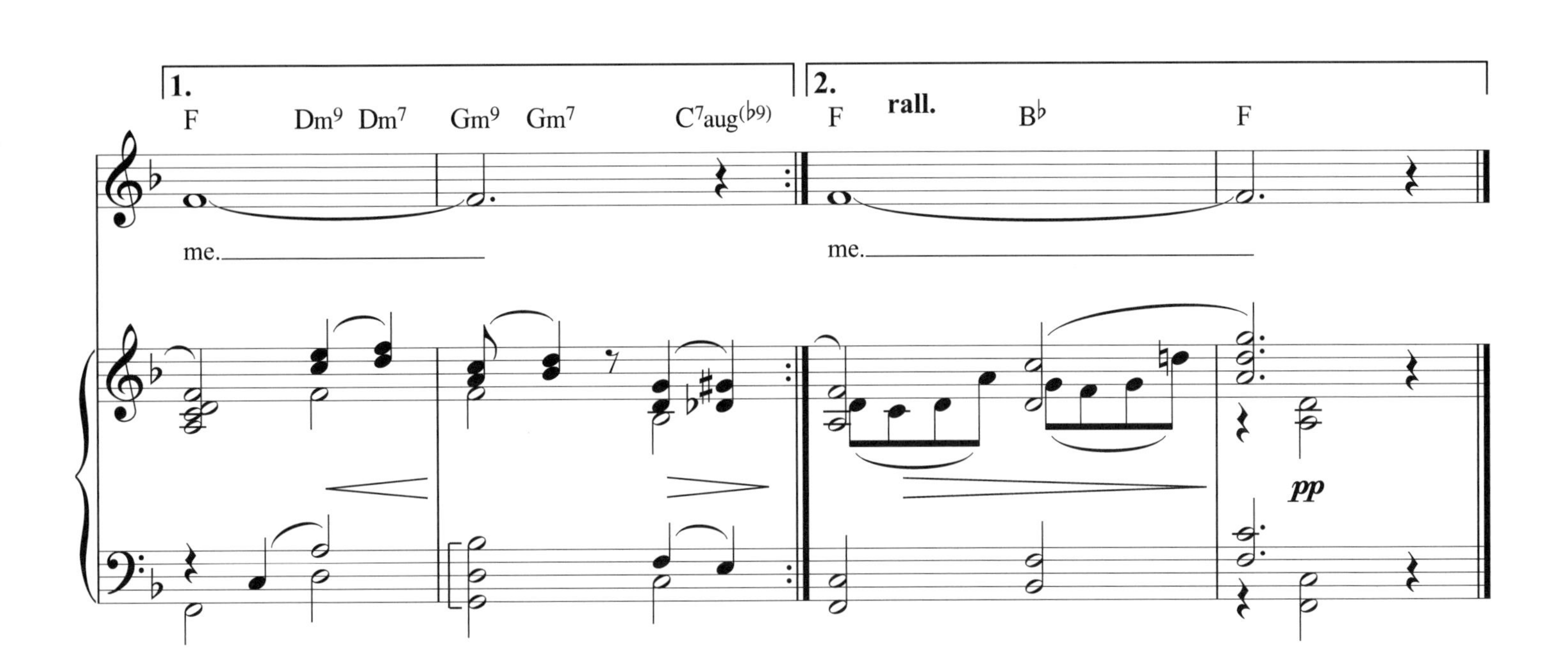
1. 2.
F Dm9 Dm7 Gm9 Gm7 C7aug(♭9) F B♭ F
rall.
me. me.
pp

CHEEK TO CHEEK

WORDS & MUSIC BY IRVING BERLIN

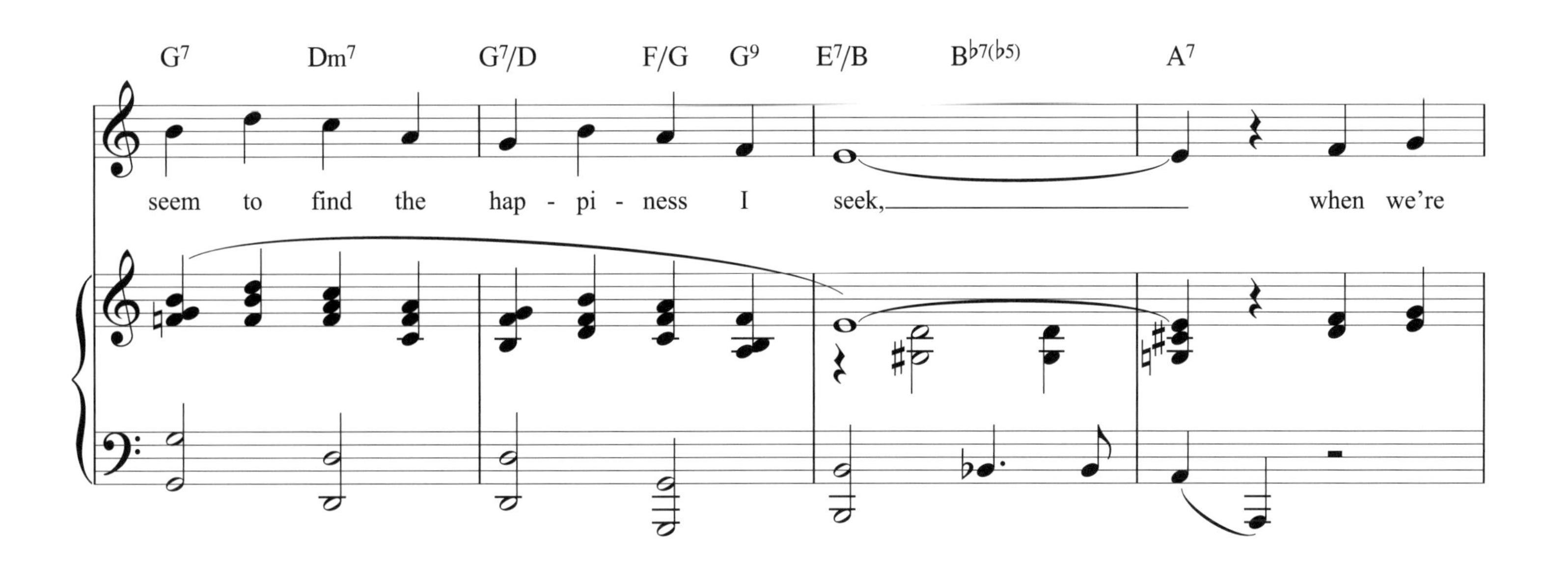
G7
Dm7
G7/D
F/G
G9
E7/B
Bb7(b5)
A7
seem to find the hap - pi - ness I seek,
when we're

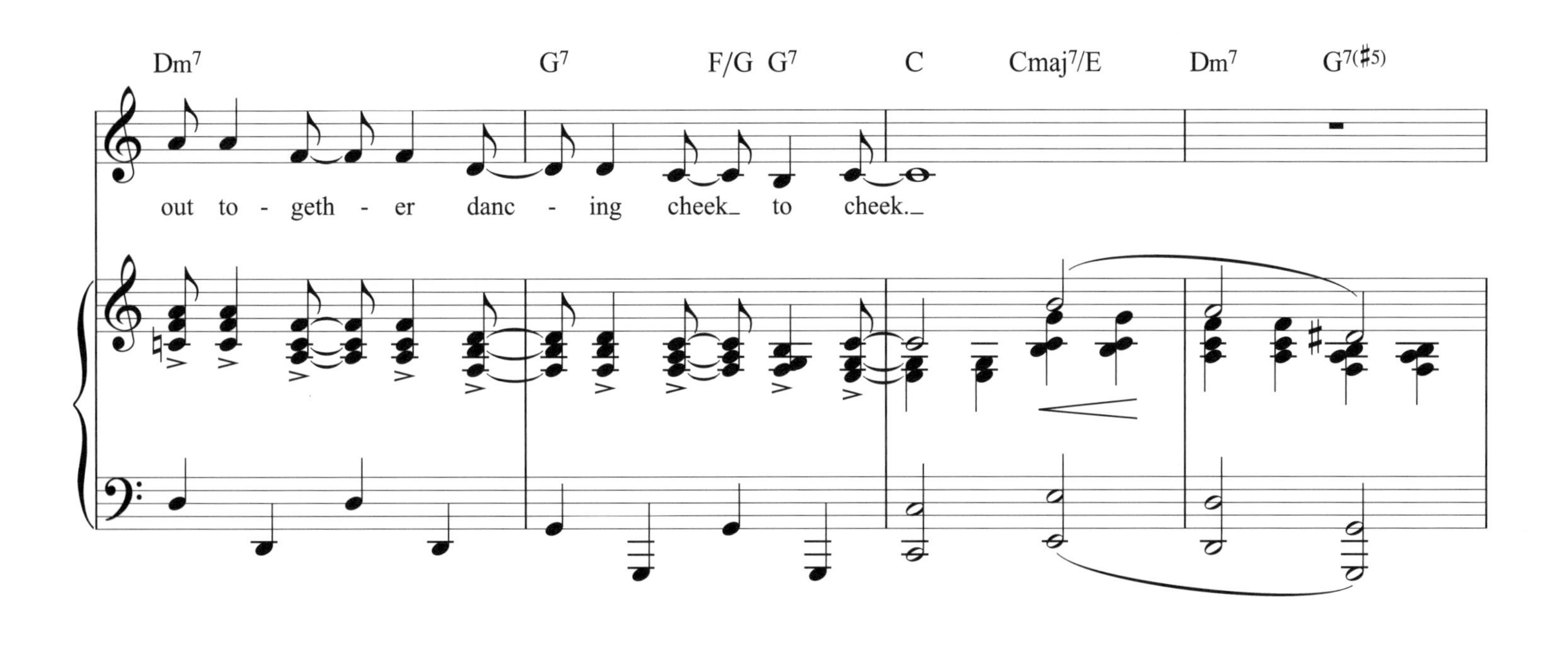
Dm7
G7
F/G G7
C
Cmaj7/E
Dm7
G7(#5)
out to - geth - er danc - ing cheek to cheek.

F/C
C
C/G
Dm7
C/G
G7
F/C
C
C/G
Dm7
C/G
G7
Heav - en,
I'm in Heav - en,
and the

C G7/D D♯dim7 C/E B♭9(♯11) A7 Bm/D D7
cares that hung a - round me through the week seem to
G7 Dm7 G7/D F/G G9 E7/B B♭7(♭5) A7
van - ish like a gam - bler's luck - y streak when we're
Dm7 G7 F/G G7 C Dm7/G C6
out to - geth - er danc - ing cheek to cheek. Oh, I
G7/D G7 C6 C/G G7/D G7 C C/G
love to climb a moun - tain, and to reach the high-est peak. But it
8vb

G7/D G7 C6 C/E Dm7 G7
does - n't thrill me half as much as danc - ing cheek to cheek.
8vb
C6 C/G G7/D G7 C C/G
Oh, I love to go out fish - ing, in a
8vb
G7/D G7 C G7/D G7
riv - er or a creek. But I don't en - joy it
8vb
C6 C/E Dm7 G7 C6
half as much as danc - ing cheek to cheek.
8vb

Cm Cm7 A♭9 A♭9/G♭
Dance with me, I want my arm a - bout you. The
f
rit.
Fdim7 G7(♭9) G♯dim7 Am C/G D9/F♯ G7
charm a - bout you will car - ry me through to...
A tempo
F/C C C/G Dm7 C/G G7 F/C C C/G Dm7 C/G G7
Heav - en... I'm in Heav - en, and my
C G7/D D♯dim7 C/E B♭9(♯11) A7 Bm/D D7
heart beats so that I can hard - ly speak, and I

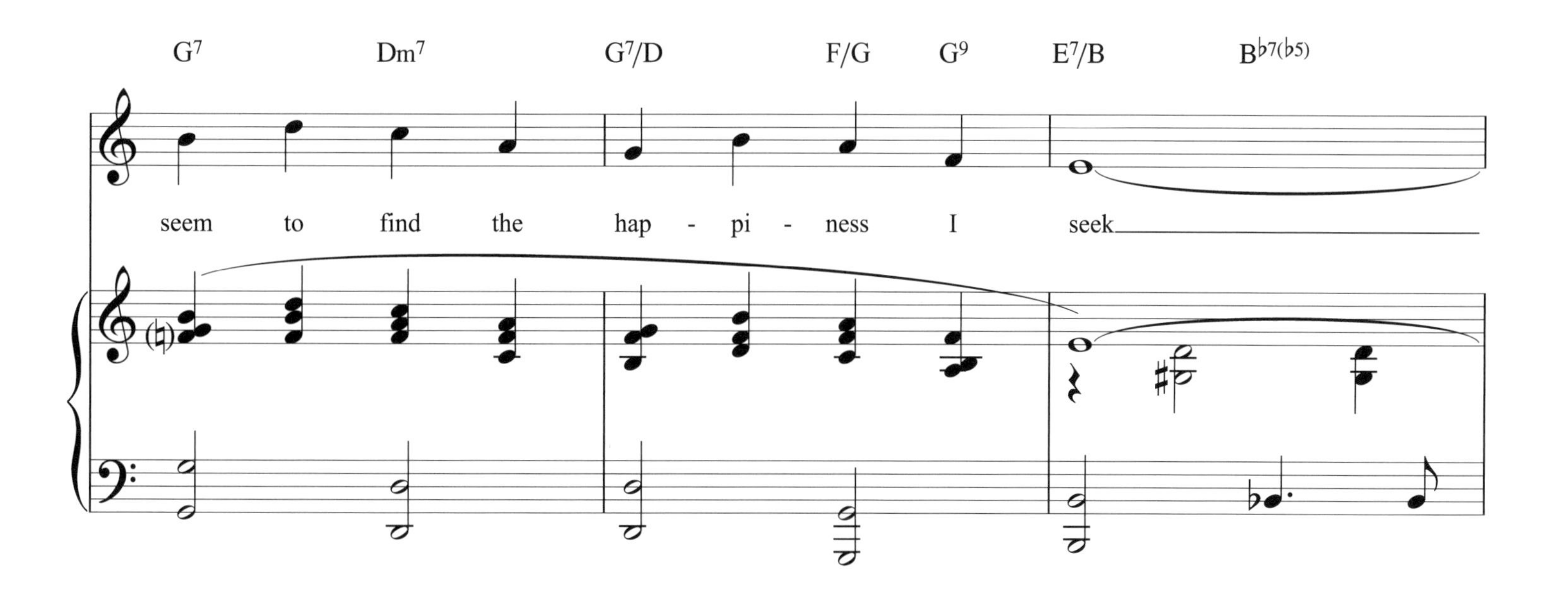
G7
Dm7
G7/D
F/G
G9
E7/B
B♭7(♭5)
seem to find the hap - pi - ness I seek

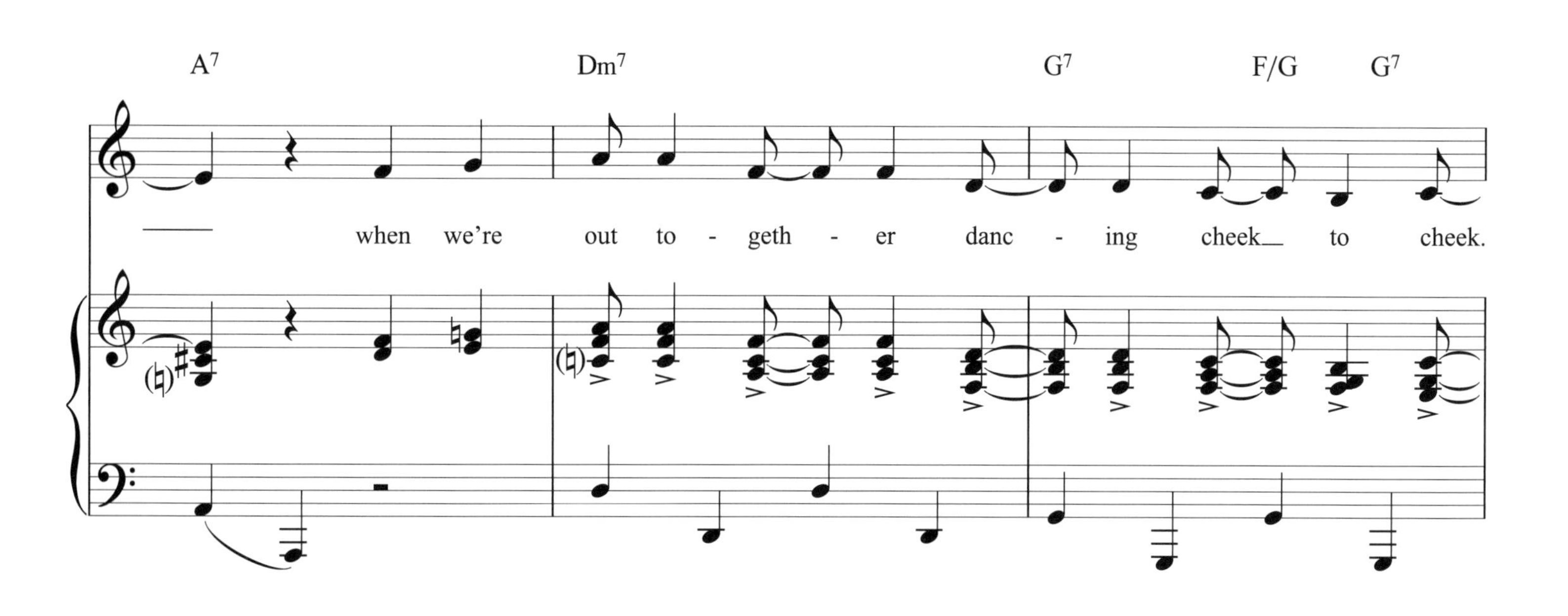
A7
Dm7
G7
F/G
G7
when we're out to - geth - er danc - ing cheek to cheek.

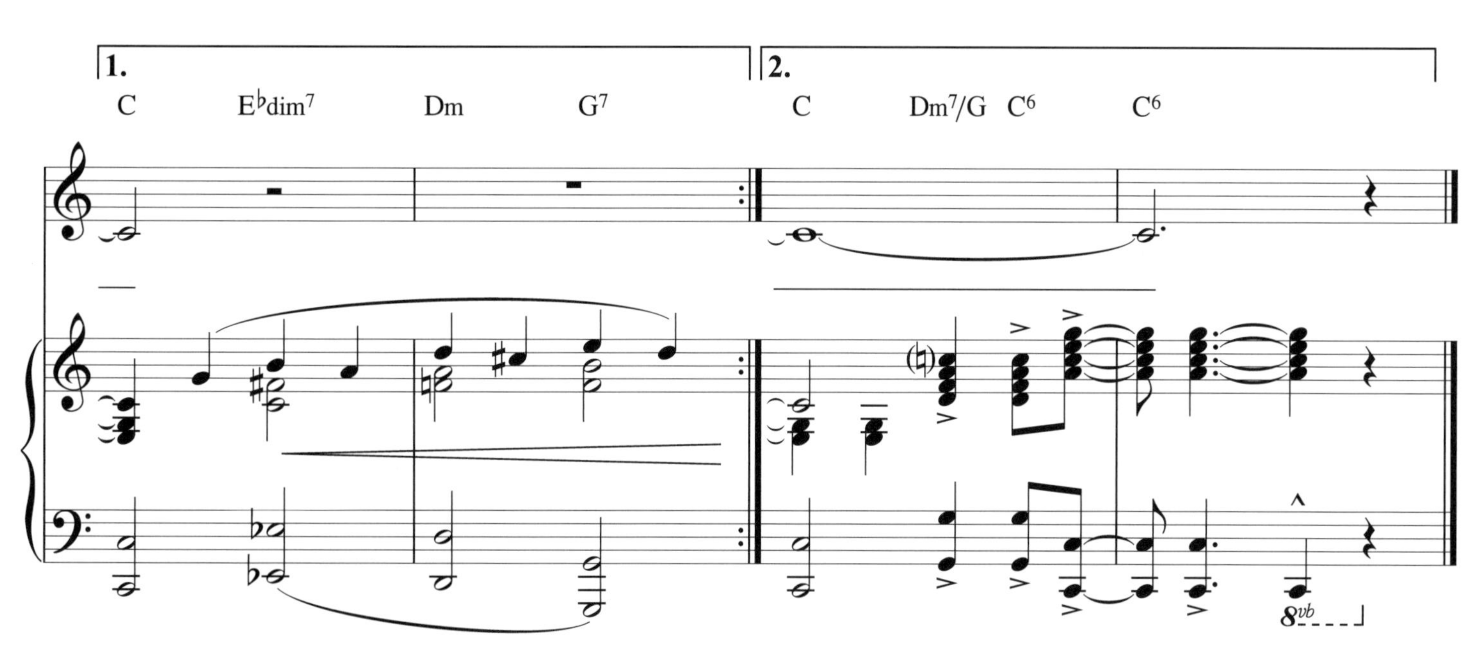
1.
2.
C
E♭dim7
Dm
G7
C
Dm7/G
C6
C6
8vb

I'M PUTTING ALL MY EGGS IN ONE BASKET

WORDS & MUSIC BY IRVING BERLIN

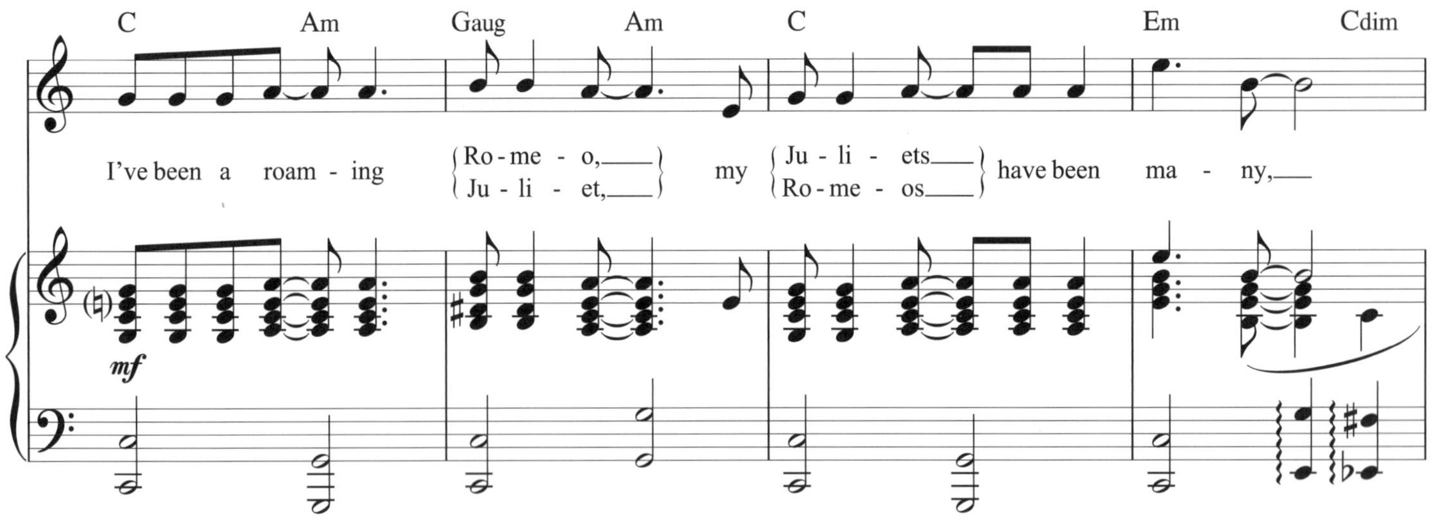

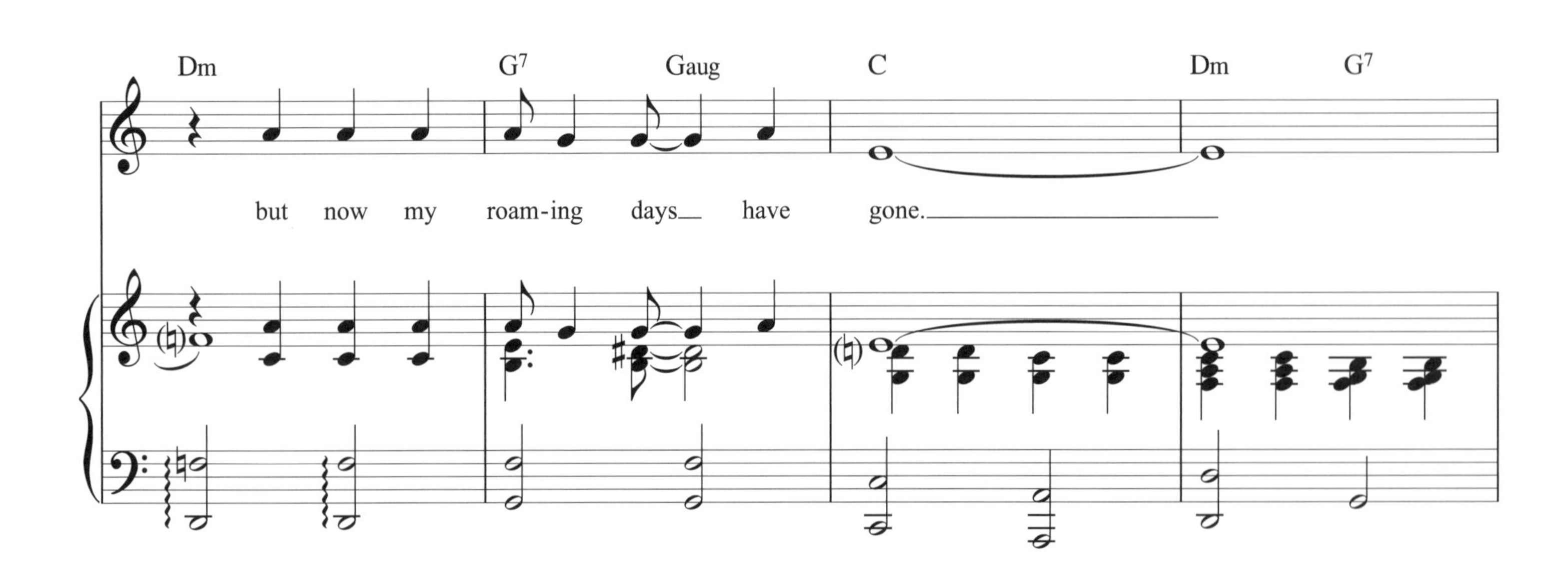

C Gaug Am E C♯m Baug C♯m
Too ma-ny i - rons in the fire is worse than not having a - ny;
D7 Ddim7 Am D7 G7
I've had my share and from now on...
C F G7 C Cmaj7 C9 F Fm
I'm put-ting all my eggs in one bas - ket,
p–f
C G7 C Am Dm G7
I'm bet - ting ev - 'ry-thing I've got on you.

C F G7 C Cmaj7 C9 F Fm
I'm giv - ing all my love to one ba - by,
C G7 C Dm C Fdim C7
Lord help me if my ba - by don't come through. I've got a great
F A♭ Cdim7
big a - mount, saved up in my love ac - count, Ho - ney, and
E♭7 G7 G9 A♭m
I've de - ci - ded love di - vi - ded in two won't do... So

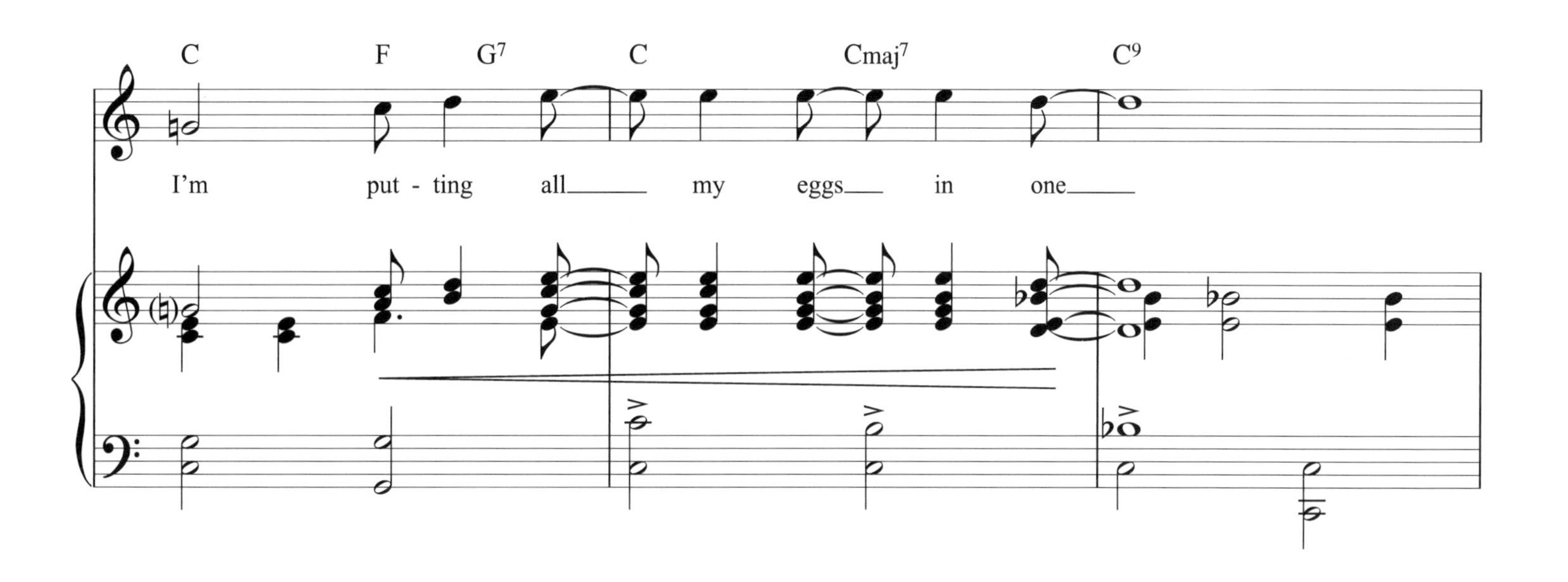
C F G7 C Cmaj7 C9
I'm put - ting all my eggs in one

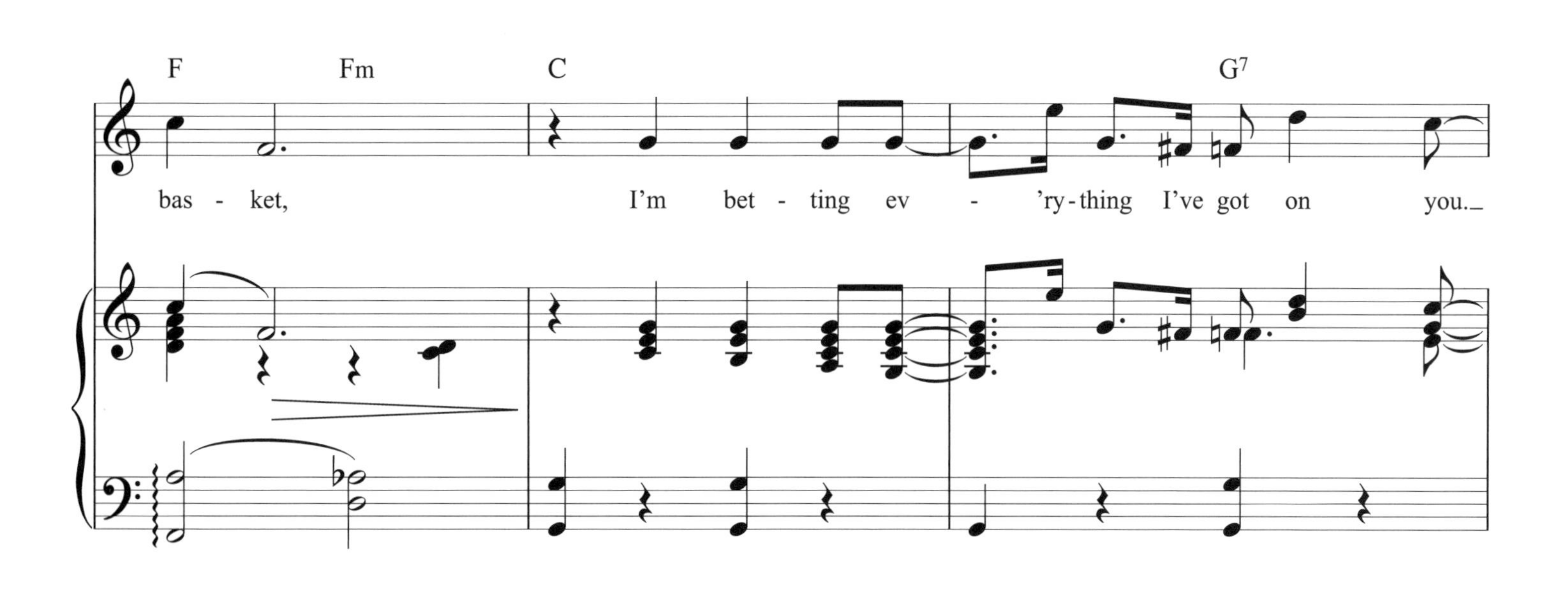
F Fm C G7
bas - ket, I'm bet - ting ev - 'ry-thing I've got on you.

1. 2.
C Am Dm G7 C F C

ISN'T THIS A LOVELY DAY (TO BE CAUGHT IN THE RAIN?)

WORDS & MUSIC BY IRVING BERLIN

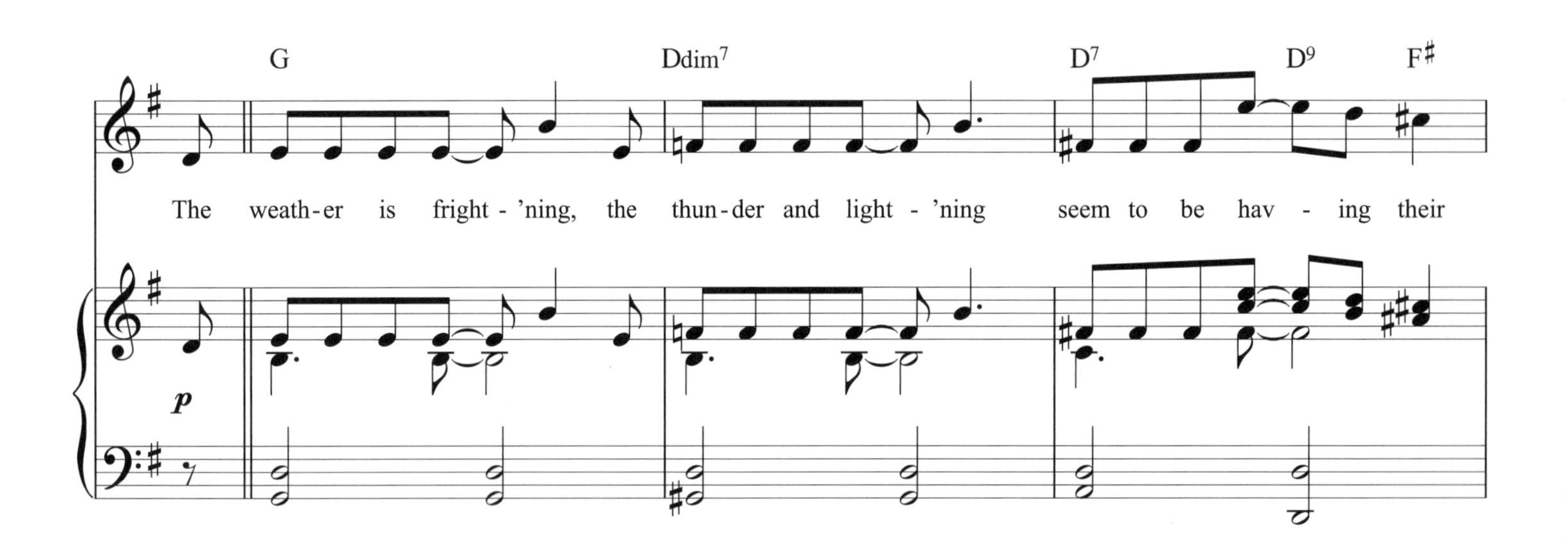

G Ddim7 C Bm D7 G Ddim7
day. The turn in the weath - er will keep us to - geth - er
D7 D9 F♯ G Bm F♯7
so I can hon - est - ly say... That as far as I'm con - cerned it's a love - ly
3
Bm E7 Am Bm G F Em Dm G7
day, and ev - 'ry - thing's O. K.
C Cm D7 G G7
Is - n't this a love - ly day to be caught in the rain?
p–f

C
Cm
D7
Em
You were go - ing on your way now you've got to re - main.
G
Gdim
D7
Ddim7
D9
Just as you were go - ing leav - ing me all at sea.
G
G♭aug
B♭
A7
D7
The clouds broke, they broke, and oh, what a break for me!
C
Cm
D7
G
G7
I can see the sun up high though we're caught in the storm.

C Cm D7 Em
I can see where you and I could be co - zy and warm.
G C G7 F G7 F G G9 C Cm
Let the rain pit - ter pat - ter but it real - ly does - n't mat - ter if the
G A9 C Cm D7
skies are gray.
Long as I can be with you it's a love - ly
1.
G Gdim7 C Bm D7
day.
2.
G C G
day.

LATINS KNOW HOW

WORDS & MUSIC BY IRVING BERLIN

G9
B
Em7
C
Dm7
G7
A li - bel - ous lie.
And who, tell me
Tempo di Rumba
C
A9
Dm7
G9
3
C
Dm7
who, should know bet - ter than I?
3
C
Am
Em
Lat - ins, they don't play base - ball,
mf-f
Am
C
Am
they're not so good with a rake or a

Dm7 G7 Em
plow. They're not ex - perts
Am Em Am
at mak - ing mon - ey, but when it
D9 F G9 F C Dm7
comes to mak - ing love, a Lat - in knows how.
C Am Em
Lat - ins, they don't like farm - ing,

Am
C
Am
you sel - dom see Lat - ins milk - ing a
Dm7
G7
Em
cow. In the day - time
Am
Em
Am
they're al - ways sleep - y, but with gui -
D9
F
G9
F
C
-tars be - neath the stars a Lat - in knows how.

A♭
Cm7
A♭
Cm7
A♭
B♭m7
E♭7
Eng-lish - men and Yank - ees, they've got quite a lot,
A♭
Cm7
A♭
G7
G9
but that ex - tra some - thing, they just have-n't got.
C
Am
Em
Lat - ins, they're so ro - man - tic,
Am
C
C9
they've got more "oomph" than the law will al - low.

F
Fm
G7
C
G7
F G7
If you're mar - ried to a Lat - in life is just
F
Em
Cm
D7
as smooth as sat - in. For a Lat - in
1.
A♭7
Dm7
C
G7
knows
how!
2.
C
Dm7
C
how!

LET'S FACE THE MUSIC AND DANCE

WORDS & MUSIC BY IRVING BERLIN

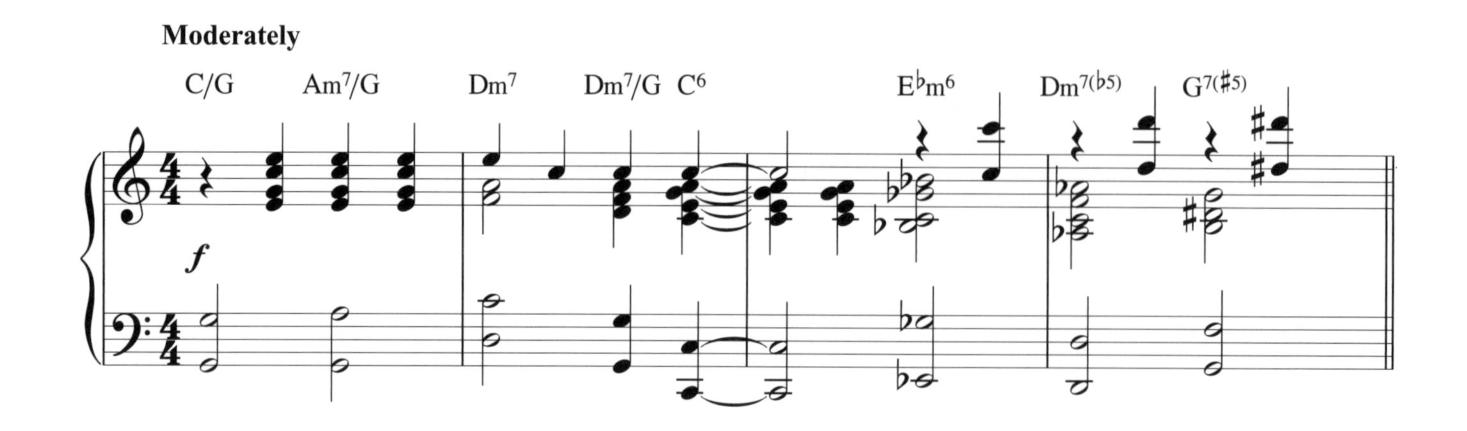

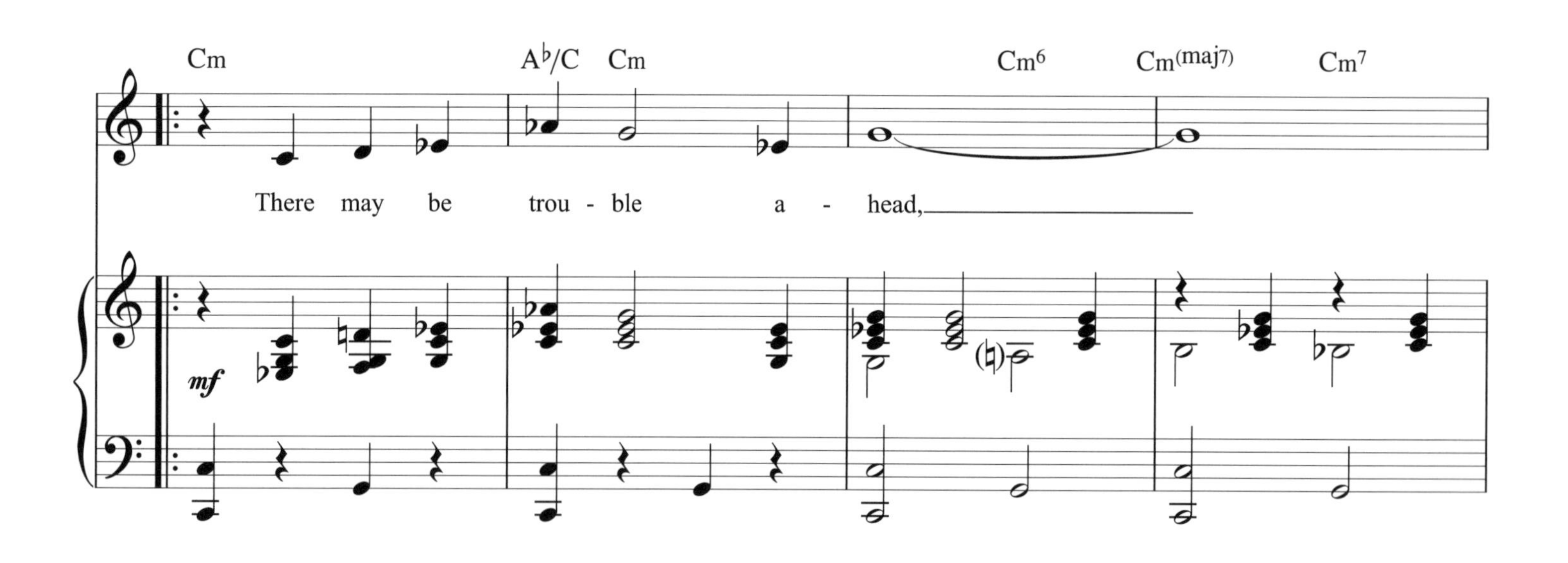

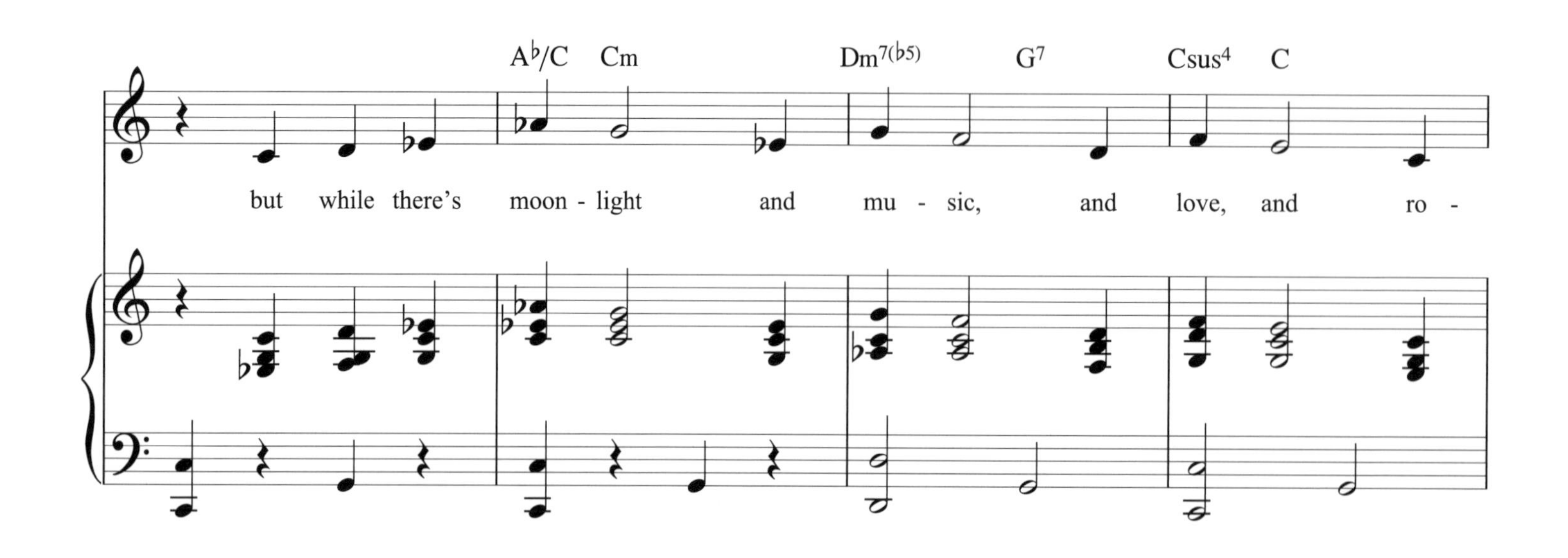

C9
F
Fm6
C
- mance...
Let's face the mu - sic and dance.
A♭9/E♭
Dm7(♭5)
G7aug
Cm
A♭/C Cm
Be - fore the fid - dlers have
Cm6
Cm7
G7/D
G7
A♭7
fled;
be - fore they ask us to
D7/A
D7
Dm7
Dm7/G
G7
F
F/G
G7
C/G
pay the bill,
and while we still have the chance...

C G6 C9 F Fm6
Let's face the mu - sic and dance.
C/E Cdim/E♭ Dm7 C A♭ E♭7
Soon we'll be with -
A♭ E♭7 A♭
- out the moon, hum-ming a diff - 'rent tune, and
G7 F/A B♭m G7/B Cm A♭/C Cm
then... There may be tear - drops to

Cm6 Cm(maj7) Cm7 Cm A♭/C Cm
shed... So while there's moon - light and
Dm7(♭5) G7 Csus4 C C9
mu - sic, and love, and ro - mance...
F Fm6 C/E D7 D7/A A♭7(♭5) C/G Am7/G
Let's face the mu - sic and dance, dance. Let's face the
Dm7 Dm7/G C6 E♭m6 Dm7(♭5) G7(♯5) G7(♭9 ♯5) C6
1. 2.
mu - sic and dance.

NO STRINGS (I'M FANCY FREE)

WORDS & MUSIC BY IRVING BERLIN

C Em C7 F Fm C Cm
I start out ev - 'ry morn - ing just as free as the breeze.
G A9 D9 G7 Gdim7 F G9 Em
My cares up - on the shelf, be - cause I find my - self with...
F G7 F Gdim7 F G7 C
No strings and no con - nec - tions, no ties to
p-f
B C Dm Cdim C Caug Am
my af - fec - tions, I'm fan - cy free and free for a - ny - thing

D9
G7
F
G7
fan - cy.
No dates that
F
Gdim7
F
G7
C
B
C
Dm
Cdim
can't be bro - ken, no words that can't be spo - ken es - pe - cial - ly when
C
Caug
Am
D7
G7
C
Em
B7
I am feel - ing ro - man - cy.
Like a rob - in up-
Em
B7
Em
B7
Em
B7
-on a tree,
like a sail - or who goes to sea,

G D7 G D7 G9 G7
like an un - writ - ten mel - o - dy I'm free, that's
Gaug F G7 F Gdim7 F G7
me. Bring on the big at - trac - tion,
C B C Dm Cdim
my decks are cleared for ac - tion I'm fan - cy free and
1. 2.
C Caug Am D7 G7 C B♭m Gdim7 C
free for a - ny-thing fan - cy. - cy.

OUTSIDE OF THAT I LOVE YOU

WORDS & MUSIC BY IRVING BERLIN

Fm7
B♭7
Cm
E♭7
I've looked you ov - er care - ful - ly,
and if I
G
D
G
B♭7
E♭
Fm7
nev - er see you a - gain, it's soon e-nough for me.
E♭
G
E♭
Gm
I hate the way you comb your hair, I hate the flash - y clothes you wear,
I hate the ground you walk up - on, I hate the phone you talk up - on,
I hate the song you sing to me, I hate the flow'rs you bring to me,
I hate the notes you write to me, the vers - es you re- cite to me,
mf-f
Gm7
E♭
Cm7
Gm7
C9
I hate the pa - tent shine on your shoe.
I hate 'most ev - 'ry - thing that you do.
I hate your phon - y "How do you do?"
your con - ver - sa - tions flow - ing like glue.

Fm7
B♭7
E♭
E♭7
A♭
B♭9
Cm
E♭
I hate the clo - set that you keep your clothes in,
I hate the ta - ble and the cloth you eat on,
I hate the fun - ny lit - tle mouth you drink with,
I hate your of - fice with the door you swing through,
Gm7
Cm7
Gm
E♭7
A♭
Cm7
F9
B♭7
I hate the hand - ker - chief you blow your nose in.
I hate the so - fa that you rest your seat on.
that pea - nut on your should - ers that you think with.
I hate your fun - ny lit - tle nose you sing through.
E♭
Gm
E♭
Gm
I hate the smell of your ci - gar, the way you lean a - gainst a bar,
I hate the rouge up - on your lips, the po - lish on your fin - ger - tips,
I hate the dim - ple in your chin, the bath you dunk your bo - dy in,
I hate the ci - gar - ette you smoke, the way you kill a fun - ny joke,

Gm7 E♭ Cm7 Gm7 C9
I hate the jokes you tell that are blue...
I hate your eyes of hea - ven - ly blue...
I hate the way you bill and you coo...
I hate the fin - ger - nails that you chew...
Fm7 B♭7 E♭ B♭m C7 A♭m E♭ B♭7 Cm7
I hate that fan - cy tie, hon - est I do, out - side of
I hate the way you sigh, hon - est I do, out - side of
I hate your bat - tle cry, hon - est I do, out - side of
I hate the way you lie, hon - est I do, out - side of
L.H.
1. 2. & 3.
4.
B♭7 A♭ B♭7 E♭ Fm7 B♭7 E♭ Fm7 E♭
that, I love you.
that, I love you.
that, I love you.
that, I love you.

THE PICCOLINO

WORDS & MUSIC BY IRVING BERLIN

D
C
D
C
- tars.
D
G
D
It was writ - ten by a Lat - in, a gon - do - lier who
Bm
F♯
F♯7
E
G♯m
Ddim7
F♯aug
F♯
A♭9
Fm
D♭9
sat in his home out in Brook - lyn and gazed at the
F♯
E
F♯9
stars.
He sent his

Bm
Em
Gm
D
Ddim7
G
A7
F#m
mel - o - dy
a - cross the sea
to
It - a - ly,
C#m
F#7
G
Bm
F#9
B
C#7
and
we
know...
They wrote some
words to
fit
that
F#
C#m
Eb7
G#m
Bm
C#7
F#
Bb7
catch - y bit
and
christ-ened it
the
Pic - co -
Gm
A7
D
G
D
G
- li - no.
And
we
know that it's the
rea - son
why
ev - 'ry - one this

D
D7
C
Em
Gm
Daug
D
E9
C♯m
A9
sea - son is strum - ming and hum - ming a new mel - o -
To Coda
D
C
D
C7
- dy.
F
B♭
F
Come to the Ca - si - no
E♭
F
and hear them play the Pic - co - li - no.

F
B♭
F
Dance, with your Bam - bi - no, to the
Edim
A7
A9
A7
D.S. al Coda
strains of the catch - y Pic - co - li - no.
Coda
D
A
D
Drink your glass of vi - no, and
p
G
A7
G
F♯m
Em
D
when you've had your plate of scal - lo - pi - no...

G D G D
Make them play the Pic - co - li - no, the catch - y Pic - co - li - no, and
D7 C Em Gm Daug D E9 C♯m A9 D C
dance to the strains of that new mel - o - dy...
D C D C
The Pic - co - li - no.
D C D
p
pp

PUTTIN' ON THE RITZ

WORDS & MUSIC BY IRVING BERLIN

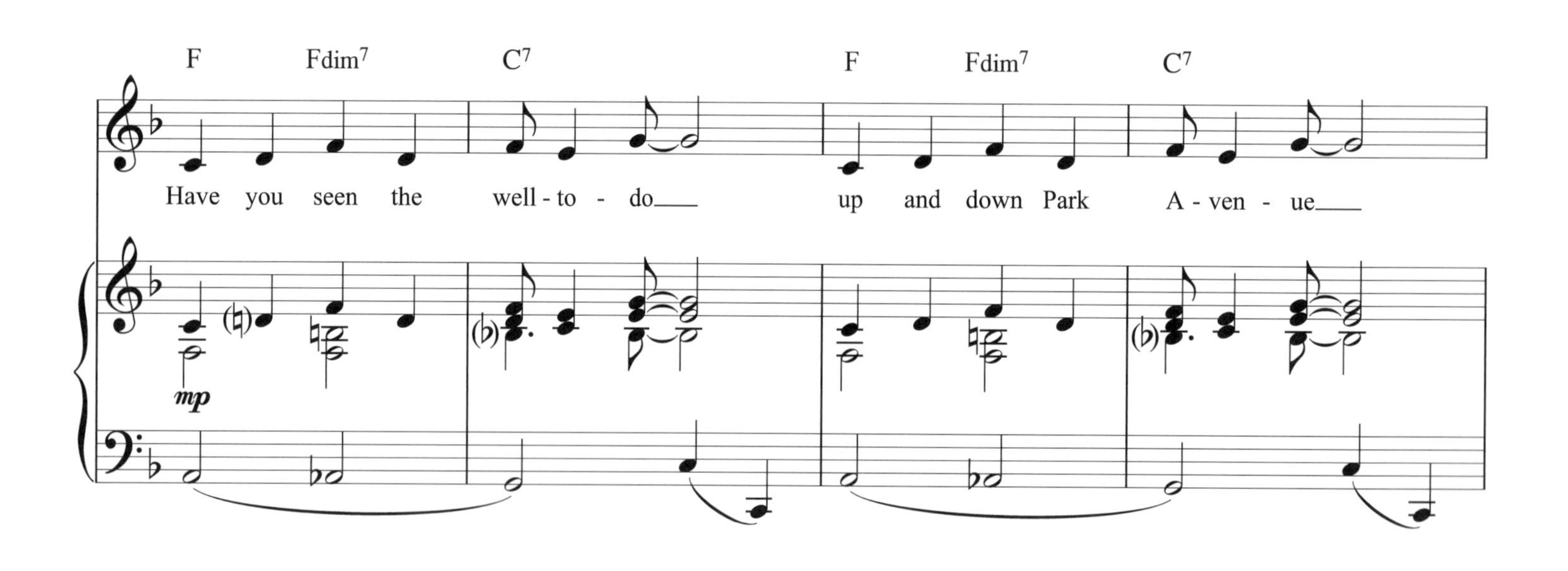

C Gdim7 Dm7 G7 C Gdim7 Dm7 G7
High hats and Ar - row col - lars, white spats and lots of dol - lars,
Am Am7 D7 G7 C7 Gdim7 C7aug C7
spend - ing ev - 'ry dime, for a won-der-ful time.
Fm C7
If you're blue and you don't know where to go to why don't you go where fash - ion
mf–f
sits? Put- tin' on the Ritz.
Fm Fm7 Db9 C7

Fm
C7
Diff - 'rent types who wear a day coat, pants with stripes, and cut - a - way coat, per - fect
Fm Fm7 Db F7
fits... Put- tin' on the Ritz.
Bbm Gb9 F9 Bbm Eb9 Eb7aug Eb7
Dressed up like a mil - lion dol - lar troup - er;
Ab Fm7 Bbm7 Eb7 Ab
try - ing hard to look like Gar - y Coo - per...

D♭9 C9 Fm
Su - per du - per. Come, let's mix where Rock - e - fel - lers walk with sticks or um - ber-

C7
- el - las in their mitts...
Put - tin' on the

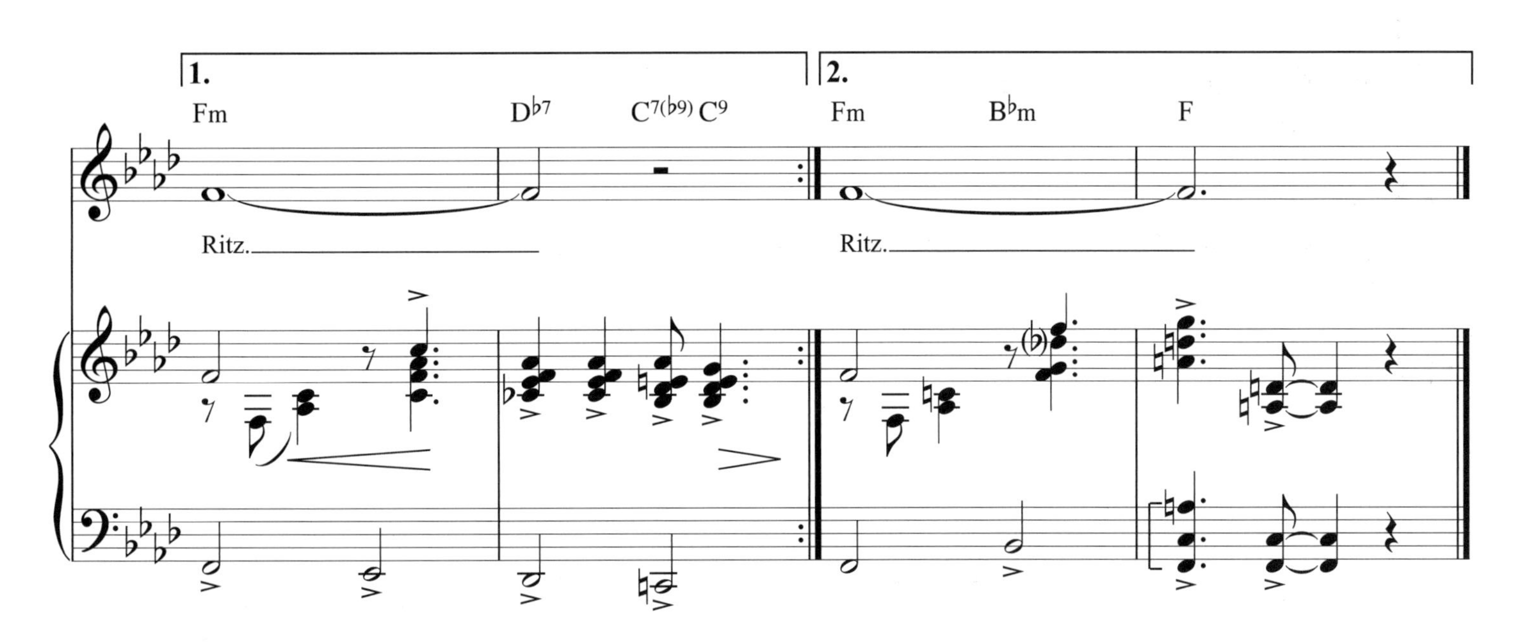
1.
2.
Fm D♭7 C7(♭9) C9
Fm B♭m F
Ritz.
Ritz.

TOP HAT, WHITE TIE AND TAILS

WORDS & MUSIC BY IRVING BERLIN

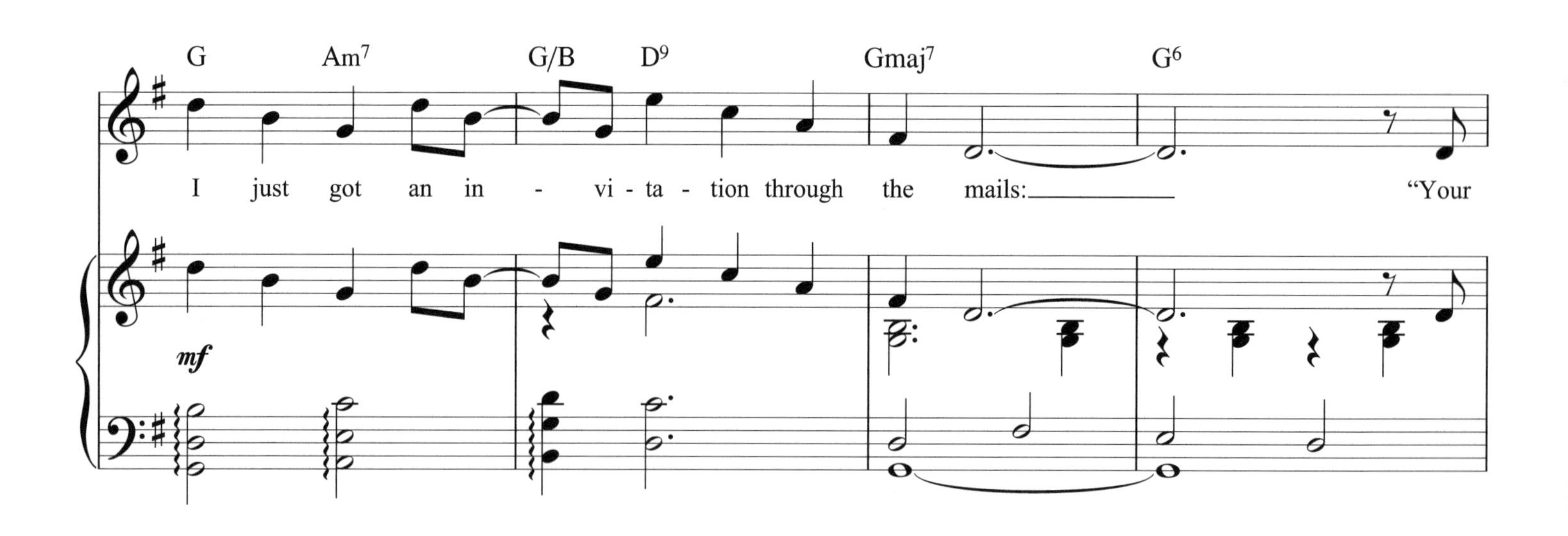

Gmaj7 G7 G6 G Am7 G/B D9
tails." Noth - ing now could take the wind out of
Gmaj7 G6 G♯dim
my sails, be - cause I'm in - vit - ed to
D7/A G/B Am/C D7(♯5) G7 G7(♯5)
step out this even - ing with top hat, and white tie, and tails.
C G7(♯5) C6
I'm put - tin' on my top hat,

C♯dim G7/D G7
ty - in' up my white tie,
C G9 G7(♭9 ♯5) G7
brush - in' off my tails.
C G7(♯5) C6
I'm dude - in' up my shirt front,
C♯dim G7/D G7
put - tin' in the shirt studs, pol - ish - in' my

C
Dm
D♯m
Em
nails.
I'm step - pin' out, my dear, to breathe
F♯m7(♭5)
B7
E
Eaug
E6
an at - mos - phere that sim - ply reeks with class.
Eaug
E
Em
And I trust that you'll ex - cuse my dust
F♯m7(♭5)
B7
E
Eaug
E6
G
F♯
G9
when I step on the gas.
For I'll be

C
G7(♯5)
C
there...
put - in' down my top hat,

C♯dim7
G7/D
G7
mus - sin' up my white tie,
danc - in' in my

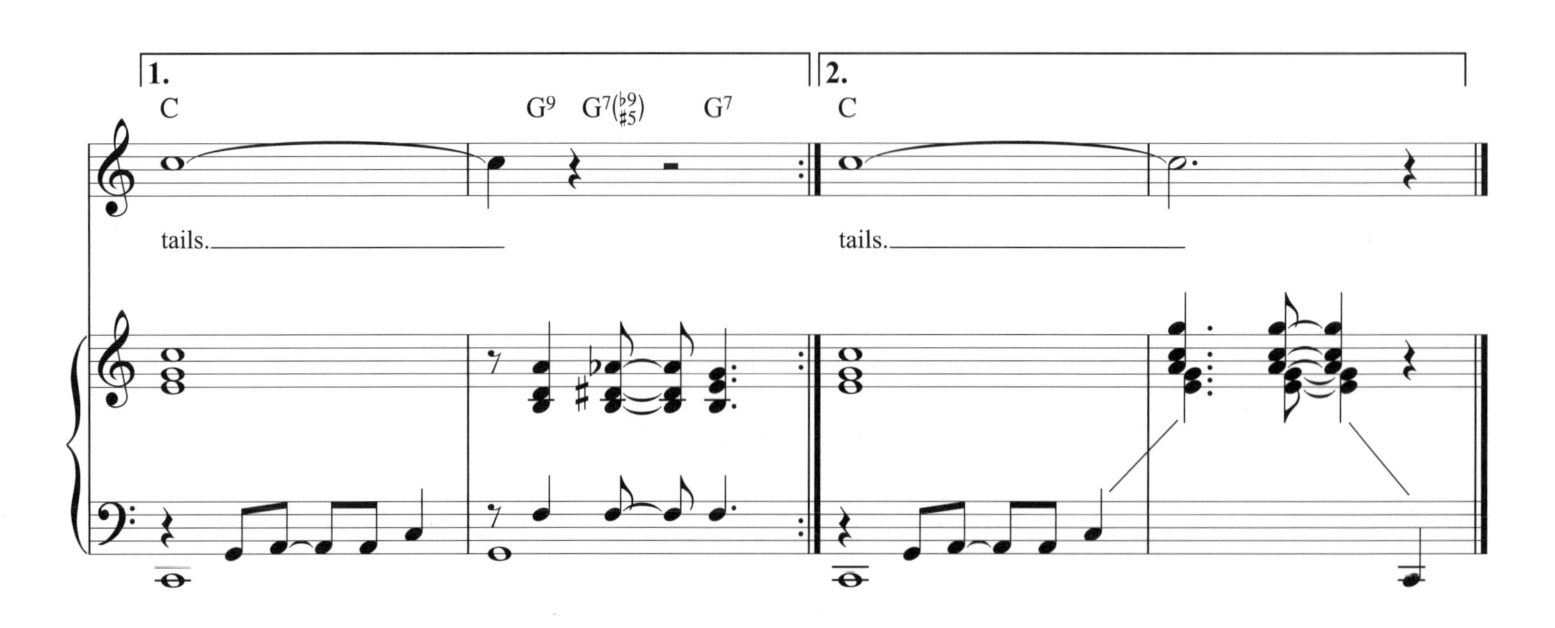
1.
2.
C
G9
G7(♭9 ♯5)
G7
C
tails.
tails.

YOU'RE EASY TO DANCE WITH

WORDS & MUSIC BY IRVING BERLIN

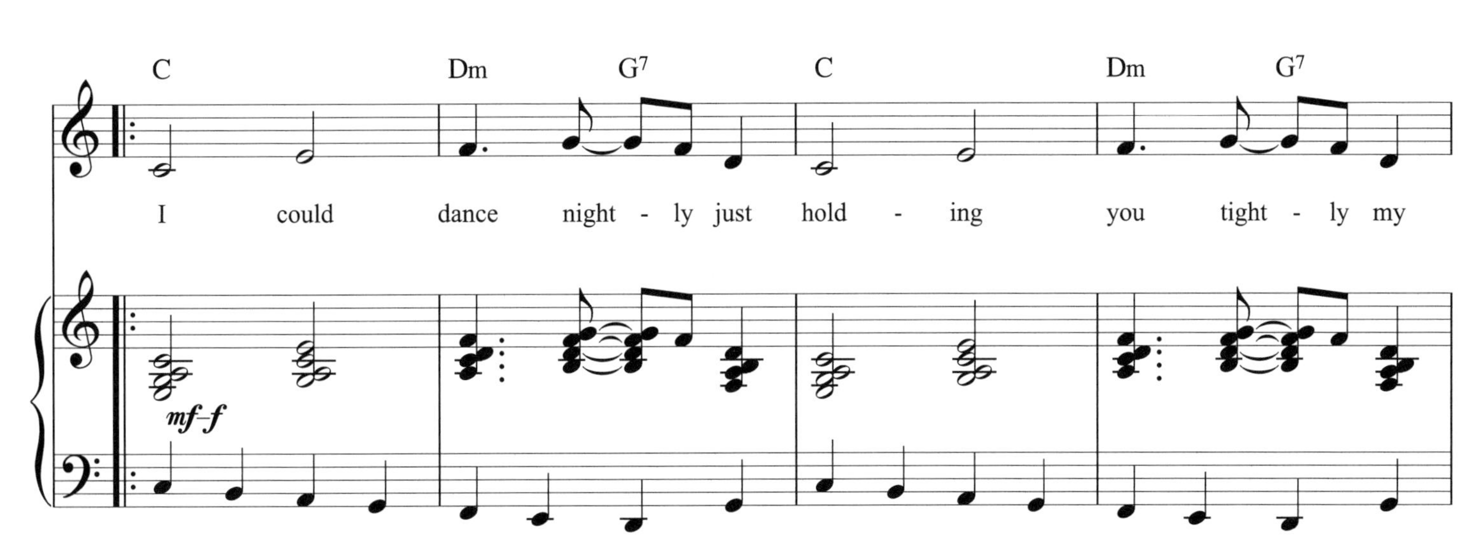

F
Gm7
C7
F
-cause you're so light on your feet.
C
Gdim7
G7
C
Dm7
G7
You're ea - sy to dance with.
C
Dm7
G7
C
Dm7
G7
There is no doubt in the way we stand out in the
C
F
Gm7
C7
crowd. Though it's called danc - ing to

F
Gm7
C7
F
me it's ro - manc - ing out loud.
C
Gdim
G7
You're ea - sy to dance
C
Dm7
C
G7
with.
Lov - ing you the
C
way I do, makes you ea - sy to dance with.

G7
Em7
That is why I'm al - ways right on the beat.
C
G7
All those charms, in one {man's / girl's} arms, make you
C
Em7
C
Cdim7
ea - sy to dance with.
I can hard - ly keep
Dm7
Fm
G7
my mind on my feet.

C
Dm7
G7
C
Dm7
C
Let's dance for - ev - er come on, say we'll nev - er be

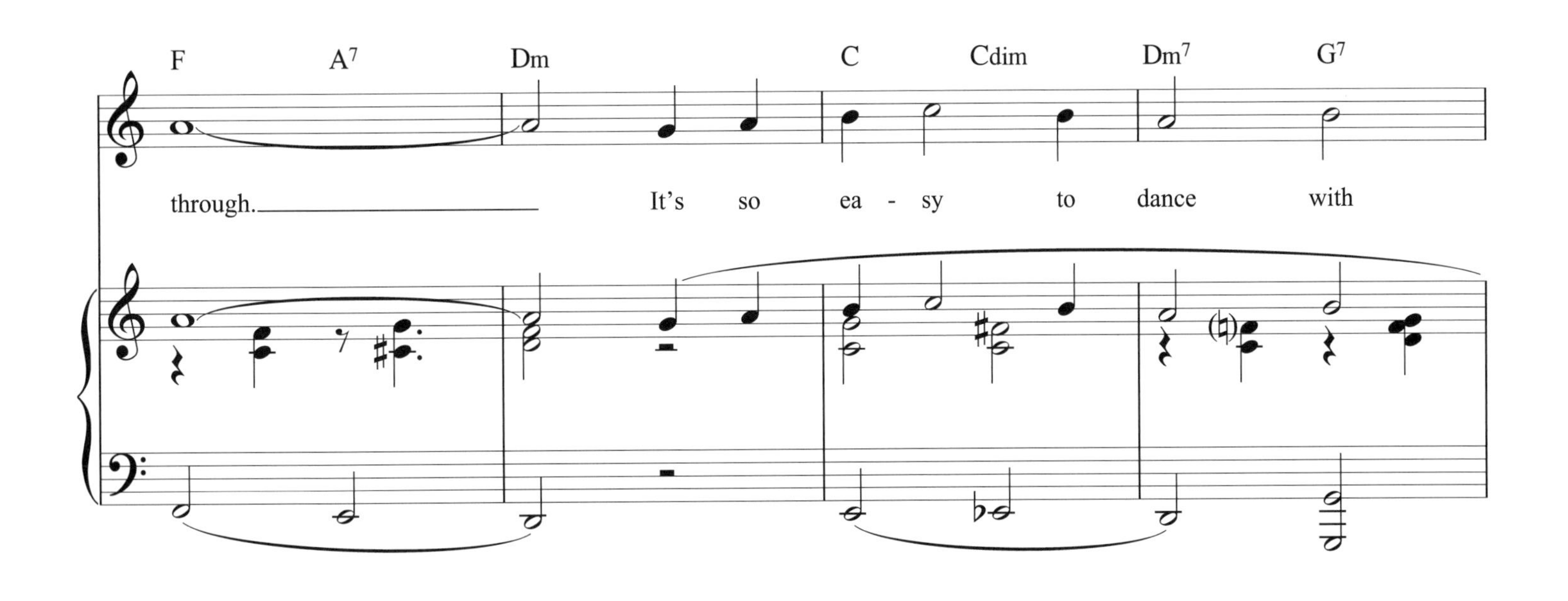
F
A7
Dm
C
Cdim
Dm7
G7
through.
It's so ea - sy to dance with

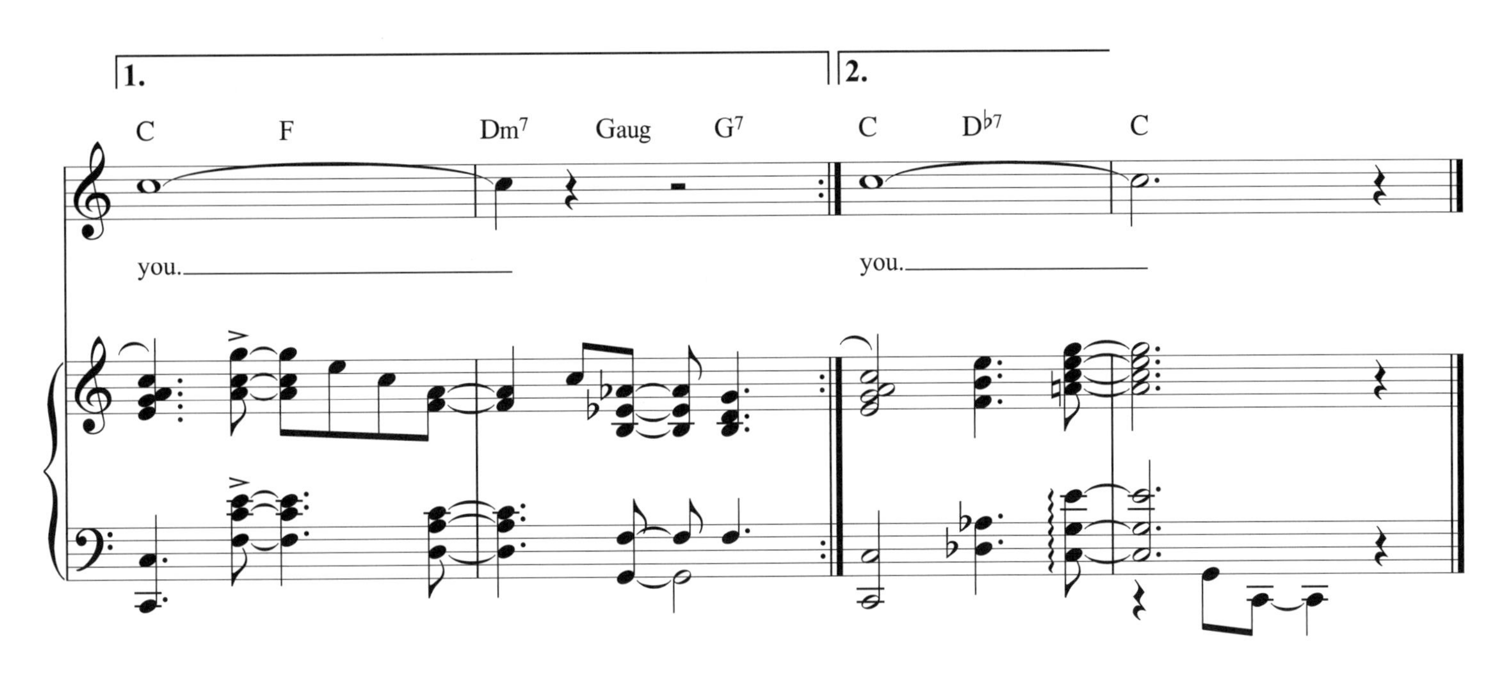
1.
2.
C
F
Dm7
Gaug
G7
C
Db7
C
you.
you.

WILD ABOUT YOU

WORDS & MUSIC BY IRVING BERLIN

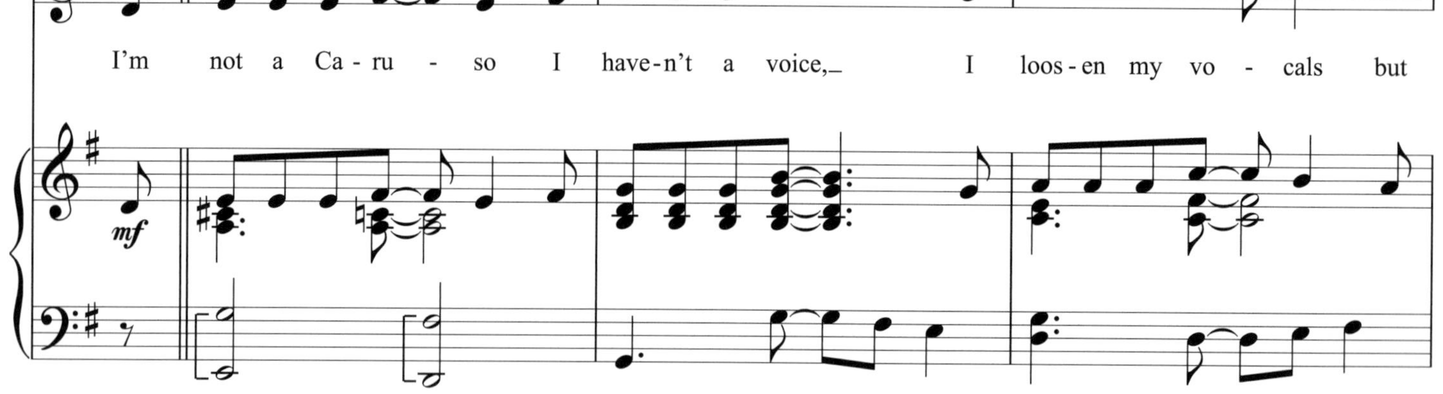

Am7 D7 Bm G A7 D7
long to sing__ it for you. It is - n't a bal - lad with
G Am7 D7 G
plen - ty of heart._ It has - n't the rhy - thm that's clev - er and smart._
Bm F♯7 E F♯7 Bm D9
Just a tune with words that rhyme,_ that I wrote to say that I'm..._
G D7 Am7 D7 Am7 D7
Wild a - bout_ you, the child a - bout_ you makes me wild a - bout_ you._ If
mf-f

G
E♭7
Am7
D7
Bm
G
I were a na - tive of Bor - ne - o,
I could-n't be wild - er a - bout you.
D7
Am7
D7
Am7
D7
Mad a - bout you, the bad a - bout you makes me mad a - bout you.
If
G
E♭7
Am7
D7
Bm
G
I were the Hat - ter in Won - der-land
I could-n't be mad - der a - bout you.
Am
Bdim
Am
Bdim
Am
E7
That's my sto - ry,
and I'll stick to it dear,
melody

Am Cm Gaug G A7 D7
in case you didn't lis - ten, in case you didn't hear.
G D7 Am7 D7
Wild a - bout you, the child a - bout you makes me wild a - bout you.
Am7 D7 G E♭7 Am7
If I were a ti - ger in Af - ri - ca, I
1. 2.
D7 Bm G Daug Bm G
could-n't be wild - er a - bout you. -bout you.

1 2 3 4 5 6 7 8 9

YOUR GUARANTEE OF QUALITY

AS PUBLISHERS, WE STRIVE TO PRODUCE EVERY BOOK
TO THE HIGHEST COMMERCIAL STANDARDS.

THIS BOOK HAS BEEN CAREFULLY DESIGNED
TO MINIMISE AWKWARD PAGE TURNS AND
TO MAKE PLAYING FROM IT A REAL PLEASURE.

PARTICULAR CARE HAS BEEN GIVEN TO SPECIFYING
ACID-FREE, NEUTRAL-SIZED PAPER MADE FROM PULPS
WHICH HAVE NOT BEEN ELEMENTAL CHLORINE BLEACHED.
THIS PULP IS FROM FARMED SUSTAINABLE FORESTS AND
WAS PRODUCED WITH SPECIAL REGARD FOR THE ENVIRONMENT.

THROUGHOUT, THE PRINTING AND BINDING HAVE BEEN
PLANNED TO ENSURE A STURDY, ATTRACTIVE PUBLICATION
WHICH SHOULD GIVE YEARS OF ENJOYMENT.
IF YOUR COPY FAILS TO MEET OUR HIGH STANDARDS,
PLEASE INFORM US AND WE WILL GLADLY REPLACE IT.

WWW.MUSICSALES.COM